For Now We Are Home

Written by Tracy Chainer Wilson

Illustrated by Jessica Banuelos

FOR NOW WE ARE HOME

Written by Tracy Chainer Wilson

Cover Art and Illustrations by Jessica Banuelos

Printed in the United States of America
10 9 8 7 6 5 4 3 2 1
Revised First Edition: September 2020

For all of the children whose
worlds were turned upside down
during the pandemic.

You are the unsung heroes.

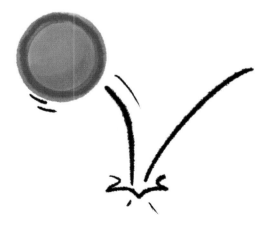

Your school is closed,
no play dates to be had.

You are missing
your friends

and the fun that
made you glad.

Six feet apart,
No holding hands today.

You can't hug them right now,

Too many germs,
so they say.

You go outside

for fresh air,

but inside you must play.

Wash your hands,
stay inside.

School at home,
family chores.

No one
knows
for how
long.

Things are strange
and unsure.

But here's what we know,
sweet child who is home,

This won't last forever, and soon you will roam.

The sky is still blue,

the grass is still green.

The flowers still bloom,

and water flows in the stream.

It's okay to feel sad, or mad,

or anything
at all.

like a
RED
playground
ball.

Some
lessons,
you will
learn.

They
will stay
with you
forever.

you are STRONG, you are LOVED, you are SPECIAL, you are KIND.

When we work together, we can change the world with some time.

Look for
the heroes—
the people
we look up to—

The doctors and nurses
who care for me and you.

The world will heal.
We will once again be together,

with our
smiles and
our laughter

ringing ever

brighter.

Like the wind in
the trees
and the sun in
the sky,

someday these will be
memories
that go flickering by.

So let's make them good ones,
with family and friends.

For now, rest,

play,

and read.

Have fun and be... you!

Sleep tight
and please
know...

The End

So nice to meet you!

Tracy Chainer Wilson is a transplanted Jersey girl who has had the honor and privilege of raising five amazing kids. Her blessings now continue in being grandma to a beautiful baby boy.

She began teaching in the second grade classroom with a degree in Elementary Education. She went on to experience the joy of homeschooling her children. Most recently, she found herself in a Montessori classroom.

Children, books, and the beach are what make her heart sing!

Jessica Banuelos is a mom to three incredible kids who have way more energy than she does. They are in their first year of homeschooling, which is crazy and exciting!

She loves songwriting, art, and cultivating the Even the Sparrows blog and shop. Some of her favorite things are singing VeggieTales songs with her kids, drinking apple cinnamon tea, and everything that has a sloth on it.

You can find her at eventhesparrows.com.

Made in the USA
Monee, IL
26 September 2020